# Cello
## Specimen Sight-Reading Tests

### ABRSM Grades 1–5

from 2012

**Notes**

1 In the exam, candidates will be given a short interval of up to half a minute in which to look through and, if they wish, try out any part of the sight-reading test before they are required to perform it for assessment.

2 The fingering and bowing marks given in this book (as well as in the exam tests) are for guidance only; examiners will not assess whether they are observed.

Published by ABRSM (Publishing) Ltd, a wholly owned subsidiary of ABRSM
© 2011 by The Associated Board of the Royal Schools of Music

# GRADE 1

# GRADE 1

**Moderato**

22

**Dancing**

23

**Fanfare**

24

**Allegro**

25

**Smoothly**

26

**Andante**

27

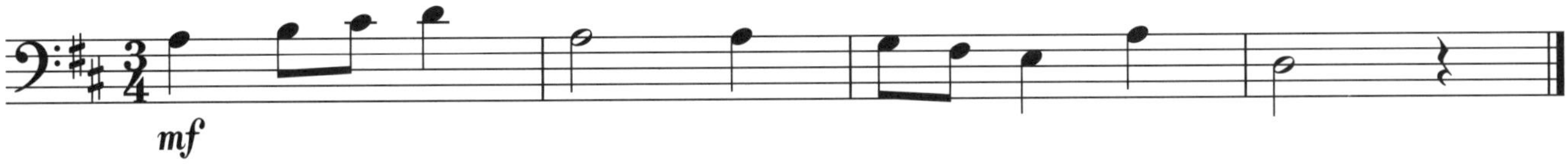

**Lively**

28

# GRADE 2

AB 3620

AB 3620

**Allegretto**

5

**Risoluto**

6

**Animato**

7

**Playfully**

8

AB 3620

# GRADE 4

**Allegretto**

1

**Cantabile**

2

**Andante grazioso**

3

**Sostenuto**

4

AB 3620

# GRADE 4

9

10

11

12

AB 3620

**Grandioso**

13
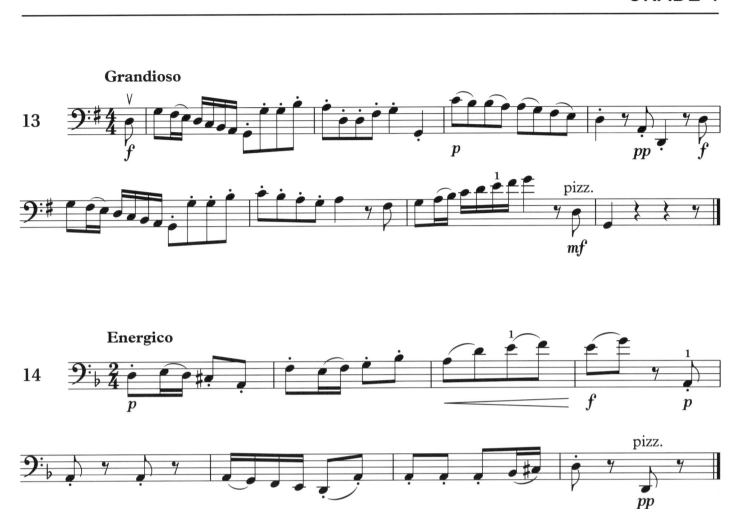

**Energico**

14

**Hornpipe**

15

**Cantabile**

16

# GRADE 4

**Giocoso**

17

*mp*     *mf*

**Grandioso**

18

*mf*     *f*     *p*

**Allegro moderato**

19

*mf*     *f*     pizz.     *p*

**Grazioso**

20

*mp*     *mf*     *p*

AB 3620

# GRADE 5

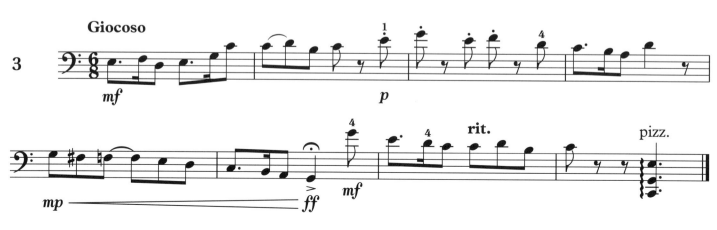

AB 3620

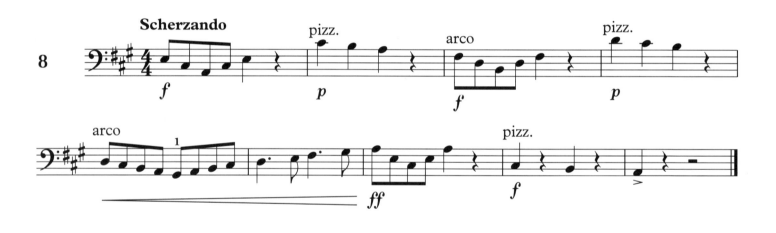

AB 3620

# GRADE 5

**13**

Tango

**14**

Valse

**15**

Risoluto

AB 3620

16

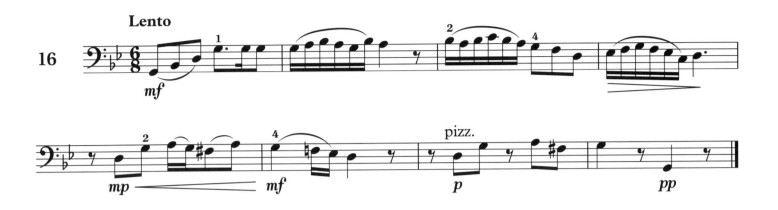

17

18

Music origination by Julia Bovee and Katie Johnston
Printed in England by Caligraving Ltd, Thetford, Norfolk

AB 3620